Other titles in the series:
The World's Greatest Business Cartoons
The World's Greatest Cat Cartoons
The World's Greatest Computer Cartoons
The World's Greatest Dad Cartoons
The World's Greatest Do-It-Yourself Cartoons
The World's Greatest Golf Cartoons
The World's Greatest Keep-Fit Cartoons
The World's Greatest Middle Age Cartoons
The World's Greatest Sex Cartoons

Published simultaneously in 1995 by Exley Publications
in Great Britain, and Exley Giftbooks in the USA.

12 11 10 9 8 7 6 5 4 3 2

ISBN 1-85015-625-5

Front cover illustration by Roland Fiddy.
Designed by Pinpoint Design.
Edited by Mark Bryant.
Printed and bound by Grafo, S.A., Bilbao, Spain.

Exley Publications Ltd, 16 Chalk Hill, Watford, Herts WD1 4BN, UK.
Exley Giftbooks, 232 Madison Avenue, Suite 1206, NY 10016, USA.

THANK YOU

We would like to thank all the cartoonists who submitted entries for *The World's Greatest MARRIAGE CARTOONS*.
They came in from many parts of the world – including New Zealand, Spain, Israel, Switzerland.

Special thanks go to the cartoonists whose work appears in the final book. They include Sally Artz pages 28, 44,
69, 75, 77; Ros Asquith page 56, 72; Nick Baker page 62; Les Barton page 35; Riana Duncan pages 63, 66;
Stan Eales page 12; Stidley Easel pages 7, 21, 27, 34, 40, 43, 48, 53, 79; Roland Fiddy cover, title page and
pages 5, 13, 19, 46, 52; Noel Ford pages 20, 50, 64, 70; Alex Graham page 61; Harca page 73; Holte page
59; Martin Honeysett page 71; Tony Husband pages 4, 9, 14, 17, 22, 29, 33, 37, 41, 78; Mik Jago pages 25,
58; Hans Moser pages 11, 31, 51, 68; David Myers pages 6, 10, 15, 18, 23, 26, 30, 36, 39, 45, 49, 54; Ken
Pyne pages 38, 55, 76; Viv Quillin pages 16, 47; Bill Stott pages 8, 24, 32, 57, 60, 65, 74; Geoff Thompson
pages 42, 67.

Every effort has been made to trace the copyright holders of cartoons in this book. However, any error will gladly
be corrected by the publisher for future printings.

THE WORLD'S GREATEST

MARRIAGE
CARTOONS

EDITED BY
Mark Bryant

EXLEY
NEW YORK · WATFORD UK

"Do we have to go through this every time
to see who does the dishes?"

"This could be a tough one."

Easel

"*Just because I can't remember what we were arguing about, doesn't mean I've forgiven you . . .*"

"Why don't you find a hobby that doesn't tax your patience as much?"

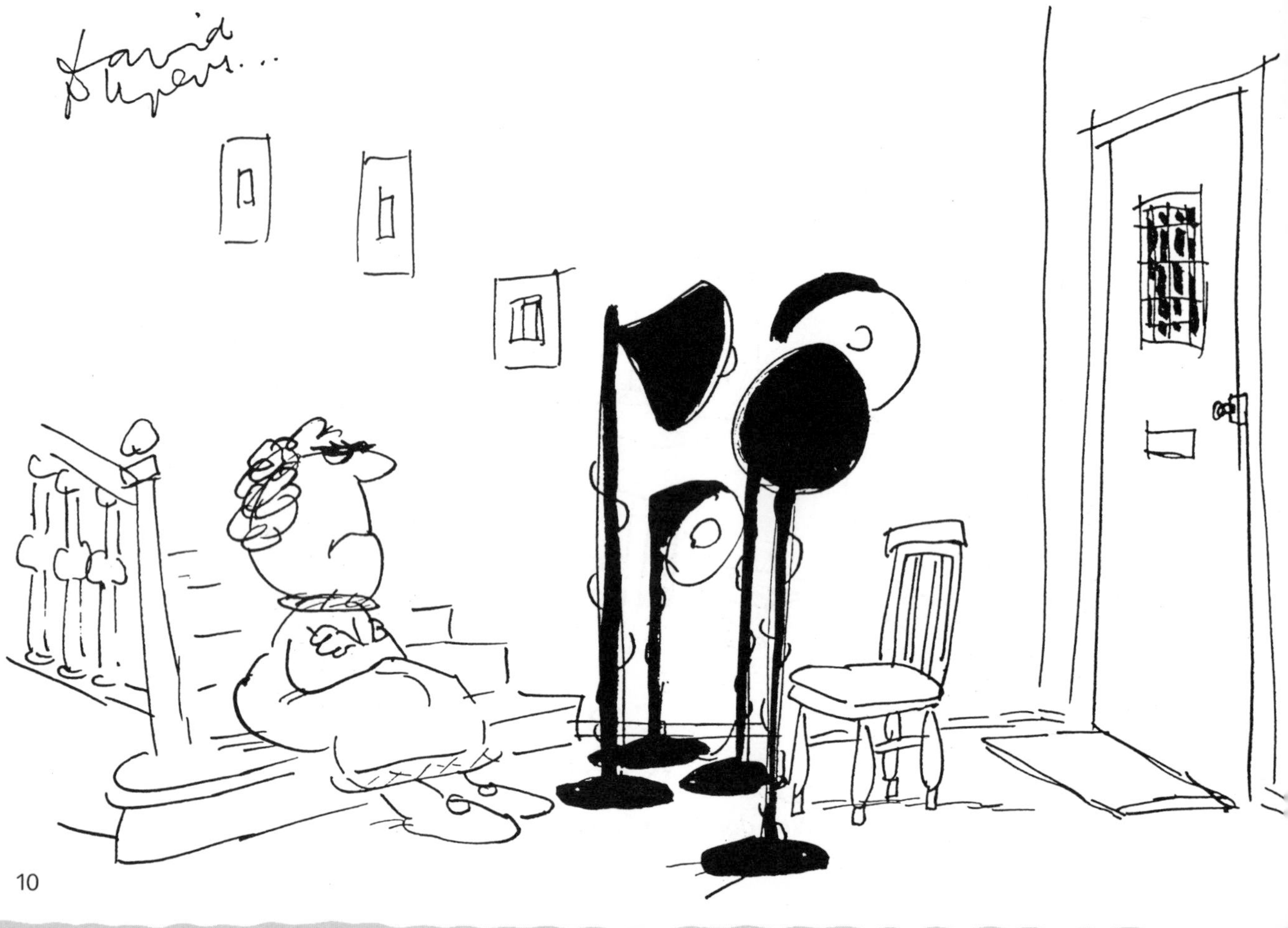

"And what kind of day did you have?"

13

"And another thing, I hate his stupid grin."

"I must go now - I think he wants a cup of tea . . ."

"Oi, sod off!"

"Alfred, aren't you a shade over-protective towards me?"

"Hello, Donald – you remember the wife-swapping party last month?
Do you think you could pop mine back when you have a moment?"

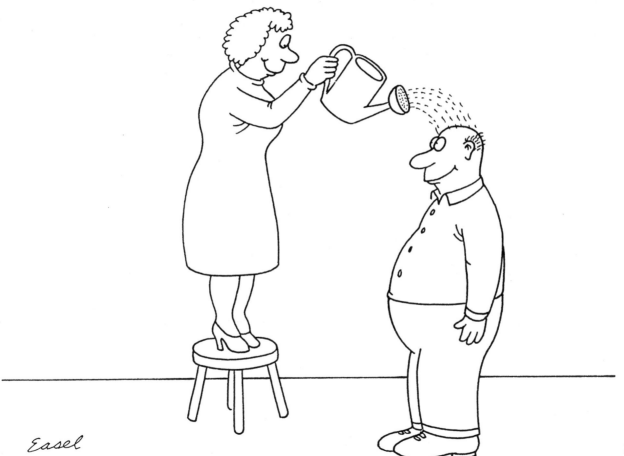

Easel

"Mr Lunt, think of your wife and eight children."

"I always show appreciation
when he behaves well."

"It's my turn to have the headache."

"How was your day at the office dear?"

"Enter. Three paces forward. Halt.
Stand to attention. Wait to be spoken to!"

"Doris loved it when Bill gave her romantic surprises."

"You're stupid, ignorant and superstitious!
How can crossed knives POSSIBLY cause a quarrel?"

"Can't you forget you're an ice–skating judge?"

"The wife's a little fussy about ash on the carpet . . ."

"I hate it when they take up a sport to be near you
and turn out to be good at it."

Easel

LES BARTON—

"It's just a precaution -
once he tried to contradict me."

"Come in, ignore the wife,
she undercooked my steak last night."

"Remember the early days of our marriage
when we still had some home truths to throw at each other?"

*"And how long have you been married to
this little squirt?"*

39

"*I love it when you roar sweet nothings in my ear.*"

"It's from the doctor. I've got halitosis."

"Bless them, they're playing mummies and daddies."

"So far as I'm concerned,
the argument was dead <u>LONG</u> before you won it!"

"Correct me if I'm wrong, but your husband seems to be unnerved in your presence."

45

"... And then guess what my swine
of a husband said to me! ..."

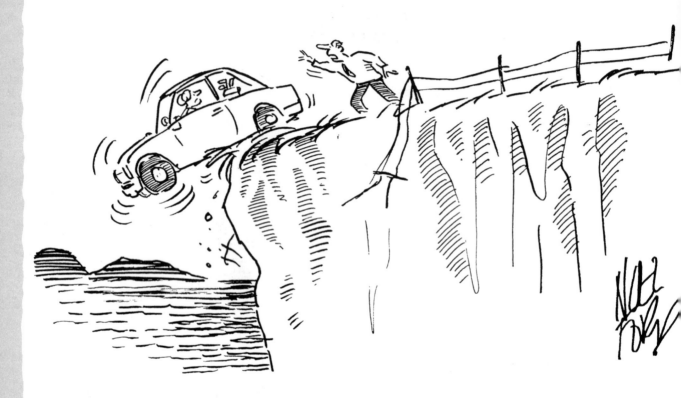

"Stay calm, dear – don't make any sudden movements –
now very, very carefully, pass me my golf clubs from the back seat . . ."

Easel 53

"What a relief - it's nice to sit down."

"Be honest with me, John - is there another woman
seeing you without your glasses on?"

"I said 'Why don't you do something for me
you haven't done in years?' He tried a headstand . . ."

"It's your turn to make up the bed."

"*Don't worry, the wife won't be back from her macramé, or origami, or whatever the hell she's studying these days.*"

59

"It's been doing that for ages . . ."

"*Good, life is passing the Smith-Watsons by as well.*"

"What's happening to us, Graham?
We never finish our arguments any more."

"Some achieve idleness, others have idleness thrust upon them, but Arthur was _BORN_ idle."

"Casserole? Again?"

"As soon as I saw you, I said to myself,
there's a man who isn't married."

"The only other thing I can suggest
is a UN Monitoring Force."

"Of course I have a good reason for waking you -
I can't sleep!"

"It's from your wife - your dinner's burnt!"

"Couldn't you take it in turns to have the teeth?"

73

"You're not going to be masterful, are you?
You always put your back out when you're masterful."

"Your advice to my first and second wives
was just as useless!"

"You never use emotional blackmail against me anymore."

"You mustn't mind Henry -
he's never at his best in the mornings . . . afternoons . . . night-times . . ."

"Excess baggage . . . just the wife."

Easel.

79

Books in the "Victim's Guide" series
($4.99 £2.99 paperback)

Award-winning cartoonist Roland Fiddy sees the funny side to life's phobias, nightmares and catastrophes.

The Victim's Guide to Air Travel
The Victim's Guide to the Baby
The Victim's Guide to the Boss
The Victim's Guide to Christmas
The Victim's Guide to the Dentist
The Victim's Guide to the Doctor
The Victim's Guide to Middle Age

Books in the "Crazy World" series
($4.99 £2.99 paperback)

The Crazy World of Aerobics
The Crazy World of Cats
The Crazy World of Cricket
The Crazy World of Gardening
The Crazy World of Golf
The Crazy World of the Handyman
The Crazy World of Hospitals
The Crazy World of Housework
The Crazy World of Learning to Drive
The Crazy World of Love
The Crazy World of Marriage
The Crazy World of the Office

The Crazy World of Photography
The Crazy World of Rugby
The Crazy World of Sailing
The Crazy World of Schools
The Crazy World of Sex
The Crazy World of Soccer

Books in the "Fanatics" series
($4.99 £2.99 paperback)

The **Fanatic's Guides** are perfect presents for everyone with a hobby that has got out of hand. Eighty pages of hilarious black and white cartoons by Roland Fiddy.

The Fanatic's Guide to the Bed
The Fanatic's Guide to Diets
The Fanatic's Guide to Dogs
The Fanatic's Guide to Money
The Fanatic's Guide to Skiing
The Fanatic's Guide to Sports

The following titles are also available in paperback and in a new smaller full colour hardback format ($6.99 £3.99)

The Fanatic's Guide to Cats
The Fanatic's Guide to Computers
The Fanatic's Guide to Dads

The Fanatic's Guide to Golf
The Fanatic's Guide to Husbands
The Fanatic's Guide to Sex

Books in the "World's Greatest" series
($4.99 £2.99 paperback)

The World's Greatest Business Cartoons
The World's Greatest Cat Cartoons
The World's Greatest Computer Cartoons
The World's Greatest Dad Cartoons
The World's Greatest Do-It-Yourself Cartoons
The World's Greatest Golf Cartoons
The World's Greatest Keep Fit Cartoons
The World's Greatest Marriage Cartoons
The World's Greatest Middle Age Cartoons
The World's Greatest Sex Cartoons

Great Britain: Order these super books from your local bookseller or from Exley Publications Ltd, 16 Chal Hill, Watford, Herts WD1 4BN. (Please send £1.30 to cover postage and packing on 1 book, £2.60 on 2 or more books.)